NICE AND SNEEZY

IN CLASS—
IT'S BATHS DAY TOMORROW, BUT ANY OF YOU THAT HAVE COLDS MUST REMAIN IN CLASS AND DO EXTRA STUDIES.

GOODY! I CAN'T SWIM AND I'D RATHER DO EXTRA STUDIES! SNIFF!

COO! WE GET HOT SOUP AND SAUSAGE ROLLS AFTER THE BATHS—NOW, IF MOST OF THE CLASS GOT COLDS, THERE'D BE LASHINGS OF SOUP AND SAUSAGE ROLLS FOR THOSE THAT ARE LEFT!

BACK HOME—
FUNNY! I THOUGHT I FILLED THIS PEPPER POT YESTERDAY.

EMPTY

THAT DREADFUL COLD IS SPREADING AROUND. SOME NASTY LITTLE VIRUS MUST BE AT WORK.

SCHOOL

WHOOSH! SNAROOSH! CHOOSH! ACHOO!

BUT, NO—IT'S A NASTY LITTLE MENACE AT WORK—

TEE! HEE!

PEPPER!

AH·AH

TOOSH!

IN CLASS—
LOOKS LIKE YOU'LL BE THE ONLY ONE GOING TO THE BATHS, DENNIS!

SUITS ME!

WAASH!

HEH! HEH! THAT PEPPER JAPE IS NOT TO BE SNEEZED AT!

BAG OF PEPPER

THEN—
GNAAASHRRR!

INSIDE DENNIS'S DESK—
DO I HEAR MY NAME MENTIONED? DENNIS MUST NEED ME!

YAASHOOSH!

JERK

YOU CALLED ME, MASTER?

SCHOOL NOTICE BOARD

BATHS TRIP CANCELLED

BAH! WHAT AN UNHEALTHY LOT OF MILKSOPS!

LATER—

ATCHOO! MUTTER! SNEEEZE! GRINDING OF TEETH

HISTORY OF JULIUS SNEEZER 55 B.C.

I'M GOING TO BE PRIME MINISTER ONE DAY!

AN EXCELLENT IDEA, MY BOY!

TO HELP YOU UNDERSTAND THE PARLIAMENTARY SYSTEM WE'LL HAVE A MOCK PARLIAMENT. YOU CAN VOTE ON WHO'S TO BE PRIME MINISTER.

THAT'LL BE ME!

NOT IF I CAN HELP IT!

VOTE FOR HONEST WALTER *THE PUPILS' FRIEND*

VOTE FOR ME OR GET A BANG ON THE NOSE!

DENNIS IS ELECTED—

HMPH! VERY WELL—YOU MAY PASS TWO NEW LAWS, AND BE QUIET ABOUT IT. I'VE BEEN CALLED TO THE HEADMASTER'S ROOM.

PRIME MINISTER

RIGHT, YOU LOT— THE FIRST LAW I PASS IS NO STUDYING, AND THE SECOND LAW IS EVERYBODY MUST JOIN IN THE INK AND MUD FIGHT!

BAH! WHAT A MESS! WHO IS RESPONSIBLE FOR THIS?

I AM! YOU MADE ME PRIME MINISTER!

PRIME MINISTER? I SHOULD HAVE SAID "GRIME MENACER". YOU'RE FOR IT NOW!

HUH! BET NOBODY TOOK THE CANE TO WILLIAM PITT!

RULER FOOLER

HAIR AFFAIR

A STORY FROM GNASHER'S YOUTH

WE'VE GOT TO SMARTEN GNASHER UP. HE'S A PROPER DISGRACE!

And so—

FIRST, A GOOD SCRUB . . .

THERE! THAT'S MUCH BETTER!

GNO LIKE!

SHAKE

GRR! HE'S HORRIBLE AGAIN!

Mum tries again—

SIT STILL NOW!

DOGGIE PARLOUR

HE'S LOVELY!

WANT TO SEE YOURSELF?

GNEEK!

THE PERM'S COME OUT!

WELL, THERE'S ONLY ONE THING TO DO!

YOU CAN WEAR A SMART COAT!

SNAP!

Later—

PATSY, GNASHER'S GIRL FRIEND

NOW'S MY CHANCE!

UNFASTEN

ALLOW ME!

THANKS!

SPLUDGE!

SCRUFFY AGAIN! I GIVE UP!

AT LEAST HE'S GOT GOOD MANNERS!

ON MENACE TV TONIGHT...
QUIZ

PROGRAMMES

LATER—

OOH, HOW SWEET, MUMSIE— YOU'VE MADE PRETTY FOO-FOO BADGES!

SO—

THEY'RE MUCH NICER THAN YOUR SCRUFFY HOUND'S HAIRY BADGES!

HMPH!

GRRNSH!

WAIL! BOO-HOO!

HEH! HEH! GNASHER DOESN'T THINK MUCH OF FOO-FOO'S BADGES!

RIP!

LATER—

AHAHA! WHAT HAVE WE HERE?

THEN—

PEACE, PRINCE OF SOFTIES—I BRING YOU A NICE GIFT— A VERY SPECIAL GNASHER BADGE!

EH?

OOH, HOW NICE! I FORGIVE YOU, DEAR BOY!

WH-WHAT'S THIS?

YEEK! A HORRIBLE, NASTY, AWFUL, TERRIBLE HAIRY CATERPILLAR!

NO, READERS—IT'S NOT A SPECIAL BADGE— IT'S A CLOSE-UP OF A TERRIFIED SOFTY!

I THOUGHT AS MUCH — BECAUSE YOU HATE SUMS EVEN MORE THAN I DO!

LATER —
I'M SURE IT'S IN HERE!
GNASHER'S BOX

COME HERE, PIE-FACE, AND TUCK YOUR EARS IN!
GNASHER'S MUZZLE

DENNIS LEADS HIM PAST THE PIE SHOP —
PIES
PIE SHOP
ALL IN GOOD TIME, MY FRIEND!
PIE PONG
LET ME AT THEM! SLOBBER!
SCRAPE

APPROACHING ZERO HOUR —
SLOBBER! DROOL! LET ME OUT!
ANY MINUTE NOW, PIE-FACE!
BOX ROOM
SCRATCH! SCRABBLE!

GOT THE FISHING ROD, CURLY? GOT THE HOT PIE? GOOD — I'VE GOT THE ROPE!

TO THE PIE-EATING CONTEST
DROOL! SLURP!
JUMP
WHAT A PICTURE — A MAGNIFICENT ATHLETE TRAINED TO THE PEAK OF PERFECTION!

PIE EATING CONTEST HERE TODAY
BUMP!
OK, PIE-FACE! GO GET THEM!

BUT —
OH, NO! UGH!
SCREECH TO HALT!
WHAT'S WRONG?

THEY'RE CUSTARD PIES ~ AND I CAN'T STAND CUSTARD — UGH!
NOW HE TELLS US!

BUT, PALS ~ I ALREADY TOLD YOU I DON'T LIKE CUSTARD — BLUP!
SPLAT!
SPLAT!

SHADY CHARACTERS

REVENGE

HOW SOME PEOPLE WOULD LIKE TO GET THEIR OWN BACK!

THE HONEST TOOTH

A STORY FROM GNASHER'S YOUTH

At the museum—

GNASH! GNASH!

DON'T BE SILLY! THOSE TEETH CAN'T BITE YOU!

EXIT

Soon—

SPARKLO TOOTHPASTE

GNEEK!

SPARKLO TOOTHPASTE

GNASH! GNASH!

SILLY DOG! IT'S ONLY A POSTER! HOW CAN THOSE TEETH HARM YOU?

And—

WHAT NOW?

GNASH! GNASH!

HO! HO! IS THAT ALL?

DENTAL SURGEON

SNARL!

PROD

THEY'RE HARMLESS! LOOK! SEE?

TOPPLE

DENTAL SURGEON

ONLY REAL TEETH CAN BITE!

YIKES!

SNAP!

GNEE! HEE!

DON'T SAY ANYTHING!

SNIGGER!

FLEAS COMPANY

FRIENDLY FUN

PADDLE POWER

HERE'S THAT SOFTY, WALTER, GOING INTO THE LIBRARY— BET HE'S LOOKING FOR A BOOK ON WILD FLOWERS!

INSIDE—

IT'S TIME I GAVE THAT CAD, DENNIS, A GOOD THRASHING!

SPORTS

THE NOBLE ART OF SELF DEFENCE

IN WALTER'S BEDROOM—

I DO BELIEVE I'VE GOT THE HANG OF IT!

SO— PUT YOUR FISTS UP, MENACE— MARQUIS OF QUEENSBURY RULES!

WRONG, PAL— DENNIS RULES!

PING!

YOWP!

THEN—

THAT'S WHAT WE THINK OF YOUR BANNER, SOFTIES!

VERY MUDDY PATCH OF GROUND

SPLUTCH!

IT'S TIME THE MENACES HAD A BANNER!

GOOD IDEA!

HOW ABOUT A RAMPANT PIE?

PING PING!

THIS OLD SHEET WILL DO NICELY—

—AND THESE TWO CLOTHES POLES FOR SUPPORT AT EACH END!

COME HERE, PALS, AND LEND A HAND! HEH! HEH!

SOON—

BEWARE OF THE MENACES

HELP! MUMSIES! SAVE US FROM THE TERROR OF THE RED-HAND!

MEANWHILE—

SHRIEK! WAIT TILL I GET DENNIS! I'LL FOLLOW HIS TRAIL!

TELL-TALE TRACKS

HOMEWARD, YOU TWO! DAD AND HIS SLIPPER HAVE A FEW THINGS TO DISCUSS WITH YOU!

TITTER!

RE HE ACES

LATER—

DENNIS'S HOUSE

PREPARE TO MEET THY DOOM

WHAM!

WHOP!

SOUNDS AS IF DENNIS HAS ALREADY MET HIS DOOM, READERS!

ON MENACE TV TONIGHT... FILMS

Later—

WHAT A PERFECT SET-UP FOR SOME GREAT GNASHING!

FOR ME? HOW LOVELY!

EEK!

BONE LORRY

YEOWP!

GNASH!

WAG WAG

ZOOM!

SCREECH!

TO WALTER

WAIT FOR IT!

But—

GASP! GNASHER'S MISSED HIS CHANCE—HE CAN'T BE FEELING WELL!

HIS BEDDING'S STILL WARM—AND HIS BONE IS ONLY HALF GNASHED!

ODD—GNASHER USUALLY LETS ME KNOW IF HE'S GOING OFF TO DO SOME MENACING!

SCRATCH

I ONLY USE THIS IN CASE OF EMERGENCIES!

SPECIAL GNASHER WHISTLE →

CRASH!

TINKLE!

EEK!

But, much later—

GNASHER'S NEVER BEEN GONE THIS LONG BEFORE—I'VE GOT A FEELING SOMETHING'S WRONG.

BED-TIME, DENNIS!

JUST IN CASE HE COMES BACK LATE.

ARE YOU READERS GOING TO HELP ME FIND GNASHER?

All over the country—

YOU BET! WE WANT HIM BACK TOO, DENNIS! WE WON'T LET YOU DOWN!

COME HOME GNASHER

WE BEG YOU TO COME BACK, GNASHER

"The Beano" GNEEDS GNASHER

We want Gnasher

OH, DEAR, WHERE CAN OUR GNASHER BE?

GNASHER COME HOME

IT'S OK FOR YOU LOT — I HAD TO PUT UP WITH THE LITTLE BRUTE BEFORE HE WENT MISSING!

FOR ONCE I DON'T HAVE TO CHASE THE HAIRY HORROR OFF MY SEAT!

HUH!

BRR! IT'S NOT NICE AND WARM LIKE IT USED TO BE WHEN GNASHER HAD BEEN ON IT!

HEH! HEH!

Later—

THIS DUMPLING LOOKS HEAVY—I'LL GIVE IT TO GNASHER AND MUM'LL NEVER KNOW.

HE'LL POUNCE ON IT BEFORE IT HITS THE GROUND!

FLIP

GNASHER'S NOT HERE TO EAT WHAT YOU DON'T WANT, DAD.

ERK! FOUND OUT!

CRASH!

That night—

WELL, I'VE GOT TO TAKE SOMETHING FOR A LATE NIGHT WALK! FORCE OF HABIT!

DRAG

IF I'M ON TIME FOR MY WORK TOMORROW I GET A SPECIAL TROPHY — TWENTY FIVE YEARS AND NEVER LATE!

PAT PAT

So—

LOUD SNORING!

Early next morning—

ANY MINUTE NOW, I'LL GET GNASHED, DROP THIS MILK AND WAKEN THE NEIGHBOURHOOD!

MILK

TREMBLE

But—

FIRST TIME GNASHER HASN'T GNASHED ME!

Much later—

WE'VE SLEPT IN — NO GNASHER AS AN ALARM CLOCK!

HURRY UP — YOU MIGHT JUST MAKE IT, DAD!

SHOVE

At work—

ONE MINUTE PAST NINE! YOU'RE LATE!

WHEEZE! GASP!

DAD'S BOSS

THE SHAME — A WHOLE MINUTE LATE!

YOU KNOW WHY, DAD!

SENT HOME

So— HEH! HEH! EVEN DAD'S CONVERTED!

WHERE ARE YOU

START A GNATIONWIDE SEARCH

Gno gnews is bad gnews

Who's gnicked Gnasher?

EVEN I MISS YOU

KEEP A LOOKOUT FOR GNASHER

Later—

I KNOW — I'LL MAKE A GNASHER TRAP.

AH! GNASHER'S KENNEL!

BRILLIANT! ANYONE CAN SEE THAT!

BUT HERE'S SOME OF GNASHER'S HAIR.

WOW! AND THE BONE I PUT IN HIS BOWL THIS MORNING IS MISSING!

WE'RE ON GNASHER'S TRAIL!

IT'S FRESH— HE MUST BE JUST ROUND THIS CORNER!

THEN—

GASP!

GASP!

I'M A GNASHER FANATIC. HOPE YOU DON'T MIND ME TAKING THIS MOMENTO!

IT'S JUST A BOY WITH GNASHER BADGES ALL OVER HIM!

BAH! THAT'S WHERE GNASHER'S HAIRS CAME FROM.

GNASHER'S BONE.

BUT THERE'S MORE HAIR THERE...

PLUG'S GRANNY'S HOUSE.

WHAT'S PLUG DOING WITH GNASHER'S OLD BLANKET?

MY GRANNY SAYS IF SHE COULD TOUCH SOMETHING OF GNASHER'S SHE MIGHT GET A PICTURE OF WHERE HE IS!

GOOD!

STAMP

HERE, GRANNY— TRY THIS!

WE'LL SOON KNOW WHERE THIS DOG IS!

NO BEAUTY

WAYEEEH!

WILD LEAP

IS SHE ABOUT TO GET A VISION?

WAH! THE FLEAS ON GNASHER'S BLANKET DON'T LIKE ME!

SCRATCH SCRATCH

GNASHER'S FLEAS

I'VE HAD ENOUGH OF THIS. NO-ONE HELPS AS MUCH AS THE READERS!

THAT NIGHT—

RIGHT, READERS, JUST BEFORE IT GETS DARK GO INTO YOUR GARDENS AND GO...

GNASHHOWL!

IF GNASHER'S AROUND, HE'LL JOIN IN — LISTEN FOR HIM ALL OVER BRITAIN!

SO—

GNASHHOWLLLL!

OH, DEAR! SOMEONE'S NOT WELL!

All over Britain, "Beano" readers are howling to see if the missing Gnasher will join in—

GNASHHOWL!

GNASHHOWL!

GNASHHOWL!

GNASHHOWL!

HOPE THIS WORKS.

But—

MY GOODNESS. FOLK ARE STARTING TO THINK THAT THEY ARE GNASHER. HOPE HE TURNS UP SOON!

Daily Blah

THOUSANDS OF "BEANO" READERS ARE SUFFERING FROM SUSPECTED 'GNASHERITIS'

EGG CUP

Meantime—

I'VE LOST SOMEONE!

WE'LL BUILD UP A PICTURE OF HIM.

MISSING

MISSING

MISSING

IDENTITY KIT BOOK

BUREAU OF MISSING PEOPLE

HE'S GOT SPIKY HAIR, SHINY NOSE AND BIG TEETH.

ANYTHING LIKE HIM?

MISSING

NO! GNASHER'S A DOG!

OOYAH!

SLAM SHUT!

OUT!

CRUMP!

HEY! MAYBE HE GOT TIRED OF BEING MY DOG AND CAME TO LIVE IN THE ZOO!

ZOO

HMM! GNASHER DID A SEAL IMPERSONATION LAST HALLOWE'EN!

GNASH!

HAIR CREAM

CHOMP!

FISH

NO — GNASHER WOULD NEVER EAT CAT FOOD!

HMMM!

GNASH!

BOOT POLISH

HE COULD LOOK LIKE A PANTHER CUB!

NO — GNASHER CHASES ALL CATS — EVEN GREAT BIG ONES!

MAYBE THEY'LL CHEER ME UP!

TO THE CHIMPS

HE MIGHT'VE COME TO LIVE HERE!

GNASH!

CHOMP!

IF GNASHER'S HIDING HERE HE WON'T BE ABLE TO RESIST THIS...

SNATCH

A CHIMP WHO LIKES BONES! CAN IT BE MY DOG IN DISGUISE?

EAT AT DENNIS'S RESTAURANT

FAST SERVICE

NUTRITIONAL ADVICE

EAT YOUR GREENS —OR ELSE.

UNUSUAL FOODS

WELL MY DOG, GNASHER, LIKES THEM.

NO FLIES IN THE SOU

SLIMMERS' MEALS

NO CALORIES IN YOUR MEAL NOW, SIR —GNASHER'S EATEN THEM.

SOON—
YOU MAY CLEAN THE CARPET IN THE GREAT HALL ~ BUT BE VERY CAREFUL.

WE WILL INDEED, LADY MAUDE.

PYE TOWERS
LADY MAUDE PYE

HERE STEADY ON, GNASHER! I'VE JUST CLEANED THAT BIT! I'M TAKE THE VACUUM.

SEE, GNASHER? TAKE IT NICE AND EASY AND THERE WON'T BE ANY DAMAGE.
SUCK

ER— YOU CAN HAVE A REFUND, MA'AM!

LATER—
LADY MAUDE'S BEEN ON THE TELEPHONE WITH A LIST OF COMPLAINTS! DENNIS IS HIDING IN HIS ROOM!

MY DEAR, KINDLY FETCH ME THE CARPET BEATER. IT'S TIME THIS OLD CARPET GOT A GOOD GOING OVER.

WHUMP! WHUMP! YEOWL!

KEPT IN THE PICTURE

MEANWHILE—

TRY AND KEEP CLEAN FOR A CHANGE!

HMPH!

OH, DEAR! THE CREAM ON THIS TRIFLE HAS GONE SOUR. I'LL HAVE TO THROW IT OUT!

I'VE GOT A USE FOR IT, MUMSIE!

WALTER, PRINCE OF SOFTIES

CARE FOR A SPOT OF TRIFLE, OLD BOY?

A SPOT? SLURP! I'LL TAKE THE LOT!

OPEN MOUTHIE WIDE! HEE-HEE!

SPLUDGE!

YOU'RE LOOKING A TRIFLE CREAMY, DENNIS! HEE! HEE!

NOT BADSH!

LATER—

NOW TO SOAK THAT DRIP!

NO—MUST SAVE WATER— SNEEZING POWDER WILL DO NICELY!

SNEEZING POWDER

TAKE THAT, YOU TRIFLING TWIT—

ACHOO! HOWL! CHAROO! WAIL!

—AND I'M NOT FINISHED WITH YOU YET!

ERK!

I'LL JUST FIT THIS LONG BARREL TO MY PISTOL!

WALTER ALTERED THE NOTICE

SAVE WATER

I ALWAYS DO WHAT IT SAYS ON NOTICES!

GULP! DAD!

SAVE WATER

ONE WHACKING LATER—

I USUALLY SIT IN A BUCKET OF WATER— BUT I DECIDED TO SAVE IT!

BREEZE!

THROB

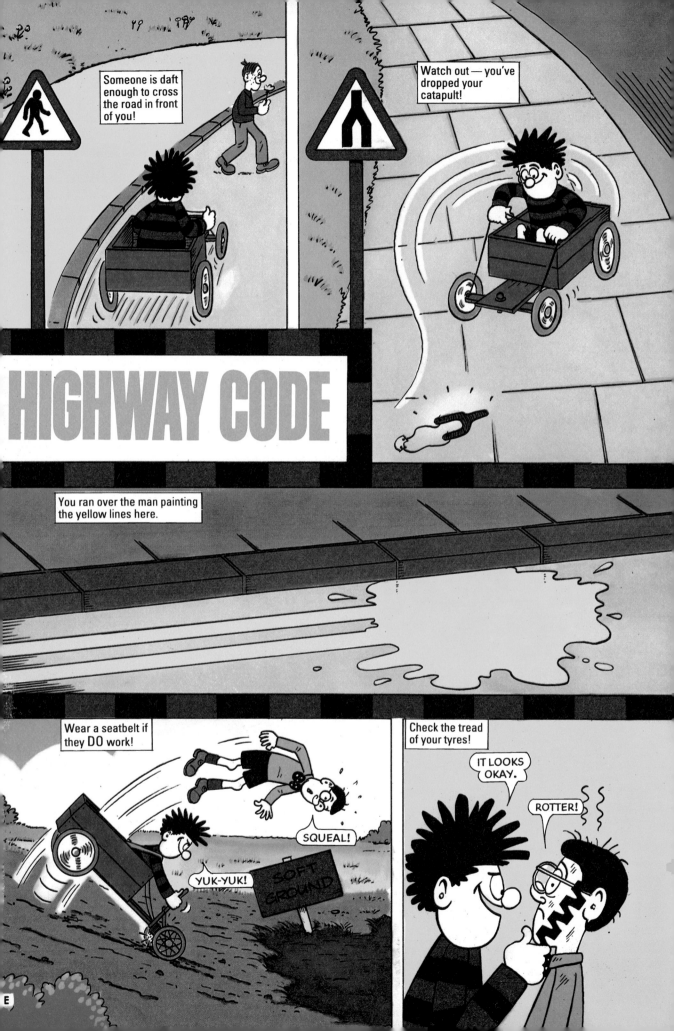

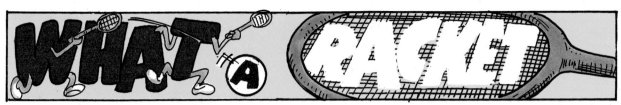

CAUGHT ON THE NOB

FROG JUMPING COMPETITION

TUCK HAMPER TO WINNER

MUST GET A FROG AND WIN THAT!

DOWN AT RODNEY'S MARSH—

HERE, FROGGY, FROGGY!

BAH! HOPELESS— ONLY ONE OLD FROG TO BE SEEN...

...AND HE'S HARDLY OLYMPIC CLASS!

ANCIENT

DENNIS SHOWS HIS FROG TO WALTER—

PAH! DISGUSTING— I DON'T NORMALLY LIKE FROGS, BUT ON THIS OCCASION I SHALL GET A FROG AND GIVE YOU CADS A BEATING!

PET SHOP

THIS IS A GIANT AMERICAN BULL FROG, ONLY TEN POUNDS.

WE'LL TAKE IT. BRING HIM ALONG, BERTIE!

COR! WHAT A JUMPER! WE'D BETTER START TRAINING GRANDPOP!

CORKS! HE CAN'T EVEN JUMP OVER THAT!

WHAT'LL WE DO NOW, DENNIS?

GLURK!

MATCHES
MATCHES
MATCHES

I KNOW! WE'LL SEND FOR TOAD-FACE McGURTY AND TELL HIM TO BRING HIS RUNNING KIT!

NOT BAD, EH?

A FEW MORE SPOTS AND THAT SHOULD DO IT.

TOAD-FACE McGURTY

CROAK! CROAK! I'VE GOT A SORE THROAT, DENNIS!

EVEN BETTER FOR THIS JOB TOAD-FACE!

FROG JUMPING CONTEST

WHAT A LOVELY FROG, DENNIS! ALLOW ME TO GIVE HIM A TIT-BIT OF A DRIED BLUE-BOTTLE.

YOU'RE NOT ON!

HEE! HEE!

JUMP

YEEK!

SCREECH!

STOP PRESS:- GUESS WHO WON THE CONTEST — RIGHT! THE ONLY ENTRANT LEFT — GRANDPOP — SO DENNIS GOT THE HAMPER AFTER ALL —

1ST PRIZE

ON MENACE TV TONIGHT... COOKERY

PROGRAMMES

THE MENACES AND SOFTIES ARE PLAYING RUGGER—

OOF! YOU CAD!

WE'LL CHALLENGE YOU TO A GENTLEMAN'S GAME REQUIRING GREAT INTELLIGENCE— CHESS!

OUR SUPERIOR BRAIN POWER WILL GIVE US VICTORY!

MY MOVE, I THINK!

SNAP!

THEN— CHECK-MATE!

YEEP!

WE'RE TOO SOFT! WHAT WE NEED IS A TOUGH SOFTY!

A SOPPY

January brings the snow,
Makes the Softies noses glow.

February brings
us sleet.
Chilblains form on
soft young feet.

March storms in with
powerful breezes,
Bertie coughs and
Spotty sneezes.

July's the time
to get a tan,
With plenty aid from
one young man.

August sees the ripened grain.
Walter finds corn quite a pain.

September can bring
mist and fog,
Which hides the deeds
of one tough dog.

April usually sends
us showers,
Especially from Den's
special flowers.

May can sometimes be
quite chilly,
But wearing six coats
is just silly.

June days are long and
clear and bright.
Extra hours to play
and fight.

...ober leaves fly all around,
...cking Softies to the ground.

November means the ice is slippy.
A time of year that's often gnippy.

December blasts will
raise the rafters,
All caused by Softies'
gales of laughter.

MASTER PIECE

LATER—

LISTEN, PALS—WE'RE GOING TO HOLD A CONTEST OF OUR OWN!

FIRST CONTESTANT, PLEASE.

HO-HO! HOW PATHETIC!

MENACE BRAIN 1977

SCORER

YOUR NAME IS CURLY. TELL ME—HOW DO YOU SCARE SOFTIES?

LIKE THIS!

SPIDER

EEK!

CORRECT!

CURLY 10

NEXT CONTESTANT, PIE-FACE—

WHAT SHOULD YOU DO WITH A STALE PIE?

THROW IT AT A SOFTIE!

RIGHT, MR SCORER—ER—GNASHER—WILL YOU SHOW US HOW TO SEE OFF A SOFTIE?

GNESH—GNESH!

ERK!

HELP, MUMSY!

SNARL! GROWL! SNAP!

THAT'S MORE LIKE IT!

LATER—

HEY! WHAT ARE OUR DADS UP TO?

WE'RE PRACTISING FOR THE MISTER BRAWN COMPETITION!

LOOKS LIKE THE MENACES WILL HAVE TO BEHAVE THEMSELVES NOW!

WE'VE COME TO SEE WALTER.

TSK! DON'T YOU REALISE YOU COULD BE OFF SCHOOL FOR MONTHS AND MISS ALL YOUR LESSONS? POOR WATTUMS IS BROKEN-HEARTED!

SO ARE WE, MISSUS!

THEN—
OPEN UP, WALTER, OLD PAL!
GO AWAY, YOU DREADFUL BOY!

RIGHT, PALS—SPREAD THAT ON YOUR FACES.
EH? STRAWBERRY JAM?

OH, TEACHER, WE'VE ALL GOT SUSPECTED SCARLET FEVER!
AHEM! AND I SUSPECT THAT YOUR SCARLET FEVER IS VERY SUSPECT!

SUDDENLY—
DOWN, GNASHER! YULP! TOO LATE!
SLURP!

AS I SUSPECTED! YOU'RE IN A RIGHT JAM NOW! GO AND WASH YOUR FACES AND PREPARE FOR SIX OF THE BEST!

EIGHTEEN OF THE BEST, LATER—
OOYAH! I'D RATHER HAVE SCARLET FEVER!

WHAT ARE YOU DOING HERE, WALTER? WE THOUGHT YOU HAD SCARLET FEVER!
OH, NO! THE DOCTOR DISCOVERED I HAD HOT FLUSHES BECAUSE MY SIX HOT-WATER BOTTLES WERE TOO WARM!
SKIP

NOW DENNIS HAS A HOT FLUSH OF RAGE—
I'M BACK, TEACHER! HOPE I DIDN'T MISS THE MATHS EXAM!
BAH! TRUST THAT SOFT DRIP! HE CAN'T DO ANYTHING RIGHT!

GATE SPLASHERS

WALTER'S HAVING A PARTY—

...AND I WANT YOU TO COME, SPOTTY, AND BERTIE, AND...

WHEN DOES THE PARTY START, WALTER, OLD BOY?

GO AWAY, WRETCHED BOYS! YOU'RE NOT WANTED AT MY PARTY!

OK, WE'LL GATE-CRASH THE PARTY! GO AND FETCH A LOG, PIE-FACE!

WALTER'S HOUSE

CHARGE!

BE OFF! SOFTIES ONLY AT THE PARTY!

GLUG! IT'S WALTER'S DAD!

WALTER'S HOUSE

OK, THERE'S ONLY ONE WAY — HORRIBLE AS IT MAY SOUND...

BACK HOME—

I CAN'T BELIEVE IT!

MUM HAS HAD A SEVERE SHOCK— IT HAPPENED WHEN DENNIS SAID—

PLEASE MAY I WEAR THE VELVET SUIT I GOT FOR AUNTIE MABEL'S WEDDING?

SOON— PERFECT, LADS! YOU LOOK DELIGHTFULLY HORRIBLE!

AT WALTER'S—

I'M EDGAR; THIS IS REGINALD AND PEREGRINE.

DELIGHTED TO MAKE YOUR ACQUAINTANCE. DO COME IN AND JOIN THE PARTY.

I SAY WALTER, OLD BOY, THAT EDGAR'S TABLE MANNERS ARE A TRIFLE SUB-STANDARD!

YUM! TRIFLE!

"NOW WE'LL PLAY "HIDE THE THIMBLE"!

HM! IT'S NOT HERE!

EXCUSE ME, WALTER, OLD FRUIT!

SUDDENLY—

GNASH! GNURK!

GOODNESS GRACIOUS! IT'S THAT DREADFUL BRUTE BELONGING TO THAT MENACE BOY!

SHRIEK! IT'S NOT EDGAR— IT'S DENNIS!

I SHALL INFORM HIS FATHER OF THIS DISGUSTING BEHAVIOUR!

WALTER'S DAD

BACK HOME, DENNIS IS PLAYING A FRANTIC GAME OF "HIDE THE SLIPPER"—

DAD'S GOT THE NOTE

WHACK! YEEEOW! WHACK!

LOOKS LIKE DENNIS LOST THE GAME OF "HIDE THE SLIPPER", AND NOW HE'S GETTING A REAL GOOD HIDING!

Ten ages

PROUD PARENT

PUZZLED PARENT

PAINE

PAINTED PARENT

PERSPIRING PARENT

PURPL